Anti-Inflammatory Diet Meal Prep Cookbook for Beginners

600-Day Quick and Easy Recipes and A No-Stress Meal Plan to Heal the Immune System and Restore Overall Health

Segin Pukey

Table of Contents

Introduction

In our busy lives, healthy eating is often put on the back burner Shopping and cooking can be a burden or a source of additional stress.It's so important to eat healthy when we're sick and our bodies are trying to heal, yet these times are often when we eat worse. The focus of this Anti-Inflammatory Meal Prep cookbook is to provide simple, usable resources for you to eat a nourishing,whole foods-based,anti-inflammatory diet without spending excessive time,money, and energy Meal prepping healthy anti-inflammatory meals is within your reach,and it can make the difference between sickness and health.

Let's go!

Chapter 1: Overview of Anti-inflammatory Diet

What is Chronic Inflammation?

Inflammation has two main types: acute and chronic.

Symptoms of acute inflammation like swelling, redness, pain, and heat last a few days.

Chronic inflammation, on the other hand, lasts for months to several years and may cause a range of illnesses.

It occurs from the prolonged exposure to inflammatory responses, even with the absence of irritants and pathogens. Some symptoms may include fever, body pain, fatigue, rashes, weight gain or loss, and gastrointestinal issues.

Chronic inflammation may lead to diabetes, stroke, cardiovascular diseases, chronic obstructive pulmonary disease, arthritis, and allergies, among others. Lifestyle changes like quitting smoking, exercising, and healthful eating have been shown to combat many illnesses.

Benefits of Anti-inflammatory Diet

A food plan aimed to reduce or manage inflammation is called an anti-inflammatory diet.

It is a combination of foods that are effective at reducing inflammatory markers or biomarkers in the body. Biomarkers, like the C-reactive protein or CRP, are substances that appear when there is inflammation in the body.

An anti-inflammatory diet is similar to the Mediterranean diet since it encourages the consumption of vegetables, fruits, lean meat, fatty fish, healthy fats and oils, nuts, seeds, legumes, herbs, and spices. Foods that are rich in antioxidants and polyphenols target the destructive free radicals caused by inflammation, which makes them your best picks.

Foods to Eat

Foods that are high in antioxidants and omega-3 fatty acids should be at the top of your list when it comes to the anti-inflammatory diet. Eat lots of the following to help prevent inflammation.

- Dark chocolate and cocoa - Opt for 70 percent cocoa in dark chocolate
- Fruits - Berries (goji berries, strawberries, blueberries, and raspberries), apples, apricots, black grapes, plums, peaches, pears, tomatoes, avocados, and citrus fruits (oranges, grapefruits, pomegranates, and lemon)
- Vegetables (especially dark leafy greens) – Artichoke, kale, red cabbage, spinach, beets, broccoli, asparagus, collard greens, and carrots
- Fatty fish – Salmon, mackerel, sardines, tuna, trout, oysters, and herring
- Legumes – Black and white beans, soybean sprouts, tofu, tempeh, and soymilk
- Nuts and seeds – Pecans, almonds, hazelnuts, walnuts, and flax seeds
- Whole grains – Brown rice, whole oats, and whole wheat
- Healthy oils - Olive oil and avocado oil
- Herbs and spices –Ginger, garlic, turmeric, cinnamon, cayenne, cloves, rosemary, and green tea.

Foods to Eat in Moderation

- **Lean meat**

Meats are superb sources of protein, B vitamins, selenium, iron, and zinc. Some even have omega-3 that can help with inflammation, such as bison meat. Whenever possible, choose meat from deer, elk, grass-fed cattle, and bison, as they have a better balance of omega-3 and omega-6. Just remember to limit your intake of red meat since it's very easy to overdo and you might end up with more inflammation instead.

- **Dairy, especially plain yogurt**

Although some studies show that dairy generally has the tendency to cause low-grade inflammations, certain people react positively to it. Pay attention to how your body responds to dairy. To be safe, stick to plain yogurt and eat dairy only in moderation.

Foods to Avoid

- Sugar and refined carbs – White sugar, high fructose corn syrup, soda, cereals, and pastries
- Vegetable oils – Corn, peanut, soybean, and safflower
- Trans fat – May also appear as 'partially hydrogenated oil' in the ingredients list of food products
- Processed food – Bacon, ham, deli meats, hotdogs, and sausages, especially those with nitrites and nitrates

Getting Started with Anti-inflammatory Diet

After knowing which foods to eat, you can slowly incorporate these into your daily meals. Here are a few tips to get you started on the anti-inflammatory diet.

- **Consider why you want to change your diet**

It is important that you get to establish this early on and serve as your motivation. Remembering why you wanted to keep a healthy diet and lifestyle is essential, especially when it gets hard or when you get tempted to fall back on old habits and food choices.

- **Load up on foods that you like**

It will be easier to take on a new diet by eating more of the healthy foods that you are already familiar with. Add a new food each week or month to get you accustomed to the taste. This is a great way to discover healthier options that may even become your new favorite.

- **Make small continuous steps**

Taking measured steps towards changing your diet for the better will bring a positive impact to your overall progress. Set achievable and realistic goals. Don't be too hard on yourself and acknowledge that change takes time. Remember that consistency is key in establishing new habits and behaviors.

- **Keep track of your meals and plan ahead**

This not only shows your progress, but it will also help you keep motivated to follow through. Planning your meals will make sure that

- **Keep moving**

Exercising has so many benefits to our health. A study has shown that people who combined exercise with a new diet plan has improved their chances of success with their goals.

Chapter 2: Overview of Meal Prep

What is Meal Prepping?

Meal prepping is planning and cooking food ahead of time, usually a few days to an entire week. There are multiple methods to meal prepping that would suit your lifestyle or preference.

You can assemble raw ingredients of recipes and freeze them, batch cook different food to reduce cooking times, or cook entire meals and store them in individual containers.

Benefits of Meal Prepping

- Saves you lots of time. You can save up to 10 hours per week from cooking and food preparation.
- You don't have to rely on willpower when deciding what to eat because it is already made for you.
- Meal prepping makes it easier to follow a healthy diet plan and eliminates the temptation of unhealthy eating and going beyond your planned portion size.
- Tracking your calorie intake will be a lot easier.
- Buying food in bulk will save you a lot of money.

Tips for Success

Meal prepping has a lot of benefits, especially for those with very strict dietary requirements such as a bariatric diet. Here are some useful tips to help you reach your dietary goals while on recovery from bariatric surgery.

1. **Create a meal plan**

   Different people have different dietary needs, that is why we need to plan our meals according to our nutritional goals. Your dietician, health practitioner, or nutritionist can help you determine what foods to eat and how much. Look for recipes or cookbooks suited for the bariatric diet to guide you with meal planning. There are also websites and mobile apps where you can check to know how many calories you'll be getting to make sure you don't exceed the daily recommended consumption.

2. Formulate a routine

One of the biggest advantages of meal prepping is that it is a time saver. Building a weekly schedule will make meal prepping easier and less of a chore. Choose a day in a week when you will go grocery shopping and cooking your meals.

3. Always buy in bulk

Choose those that do not spoil easily or can be stored in the freezer. Organic quinoa, light brown rice, olive oil, and frozen vegetables can be purchased in bulk to last you a few months. Buying produce that is in season will also help you save money.

4. Invest in good quality cooking utensils and appliances

There are several multi-cookers available in the market today to make cooking a breeze and further cut cooking times. Big pots and pans are excellent for cooking large batches of food at a time. A food processor or vegetable slicer will also come in handy for meal preps.

5. Choose a meal prep style that suits you

You can prep entire meals that only need re-heating, or you can batch cook several ingredients separately to cut down on cooking times.

6. Get plenty storage

Opt for glass containers for your pre-prepared meals. You may also go for air-tight plastic containers, just make sure that it is BPA-free if you plan on microwaving your meals in them. Stainless steel food containers are also excellent choices.

Glass mason jars also come in handy for storing wet and dry ingredients like grains and dressings. Try silicone baggies and beeswax wraps to lessen your plastic use, they are perfect for snacking on-the-go. Also, get stackable versions of these containers to save space on your fridge.

7. Label your foods

With so many containers in your fridge, it's easy to forget some and end up with spoiled food. To make it easier to keep track and mainly for safety, make it a habit of marking or using labels to make sure you consume them promptly. You may also use your phone calendar to list your daily meals and set a reminder. Knowing about food safety measures is an important thing to consider when you are meal prepping while on a bariatric diet. Read it to guide you with the right cooking temperatures for different foods and learn about other best practices.

8. Don't mix the sauce or dressing with the dry ingredients

Pouring sauces over your cooked chicken or rice will make it soggy. Unless you are aiming for this kind of texture, store wet ingredients in mason jars.

9. Prepare snacks too

You don't have to stick to meals. Pre-packing snacks for whenever you get hungry in between meals are equally important as it keeps you from eating anything that might upset your stomach or mess with your goals.

10. Try shopping online

Look for businesses that offer this option around your area. You may also ask your local supermarket if they have this option available. Not only is this convenient, but you'll further cut down on costs if you do your shopping online. Also, it is much less tempting to go beyond your grocery list and budget versus being physically at the store.

Chapter 3: 3-Week Meal Plan to Start Your Journey

Week 1

Sunday

Breakfast: Breakfast avocado boat

Lunch: Meatball

Dinner: Lemon pepper shrimp

Monday

Breakfast: Breakfast Frittata

Lunch: Crumbed fish

Dinner: Zucchini marinara

Tuesday

Breakfast: Brussels sprouts

Lunch: Chicken thighs

Dinner: Crispy garlic shrimp

Wednesday

Breakfast: Breakfast Tofu

Lunch: Salmon cakes

Dinner: Steak & mushrooms

Thursday

Breakfast: Breakfast casserole

Lunch: Coconut shrimp

Dinner: Crispy chicken tenderloin

Friday

Breakfast: Breakfast omelet

Lunch: Cajun salmon

Dinner: Meatloaf

Saturday

Breakfast: Breakfast potatoes

Lunch: Scallops

Dinner: Mushroom pizza

Week 2

Sunday

Breakfast: Breakfast stuffed biscuits

Lunch: Crispy eggplant parmesan

Dinner: Lemon pepper shrimp

Monday

Breakfast: Sweet potato hash

Lunch: Fish patties

Dinner: Steak & mushrooms

Tuesday

Breakfast: Artichoke hearts

Lunch: Chicken taquitos

Dinner: Mexican fish

Wednesday

Breakfast: Baked potatoes

Lunch: Stuffed peppers

Dinner: Lime & chili salmon

Thursday

Breakfast: Breakfast omelet

Lunch: Crispy shrimp

Dinner: Honey roasted carrots

Friday

Breakfast: Breakfast avocado boat

Lunch: Turkey breast tenderloin

Dinner: Shrimp bang bang

Saturday

Breakfast: Tex-Mex hash browns

Lunch: Stuffed mushrooms

Dinner: Southern style chicken

Week 3

Sunday

Breakfast: Breakfast sandwich

Lunch: Roasted okra

Dinner: Coconut crusted fish strips

Monday

Breakfast: Breakfast casserole

Lunch: Crispy chicken tenders

Dinner: Buffalo cauliflower

Tuesday

Breakfast: Breakfast omelet

Lunch: Beef tips

Dinner: Chicken katsu

Wednesday

Breakfast: Garlic baby potatoes

Lunch: Chicken breast

Dinner: Garlic cauliflower

Thursday

Breakfast: Breakfast stuffed biscuits

Lunch: Fish tacos

Dinner: Roasted whole chicken

Friday

Breakfast: Breakfast tofu

Lunch: Spicy green beans

Dinner: Popcorn shrimp

Saturday

Breakfast: Tex-Mex hash browns

Lunch: Parmesan chicken

Dinner: Steak with asparagus

Chapter 4: Breakfast

Breakfast Casserole

Preparation Time: 10 minutes

Cooking Time: 10 minutes

Servings: 4

Ingredients:

- 1 lb. hash browns
- 1 lb. lean breakfast sausage, crumbled
- 1 yellow onion, chopped
- 1 red bell pepper, chopped
- 1 yellow bell pepper, chopped
- 1 green bell pepper, chopped
- Pepper to taste

Method:

1. Arrange hash browns in the air fryer basket.
2. Top with sausage and veggies.
3. Air fry at 355 degrees F for 10 minutes.
4. Season with pepper.

Serving Suggestions: Garnish with chopped fresh herbs.

Preparation & Cooking Tips: You can also add mushrooms to this recipe.

Breakfast Avocado Boat

Preparation Time: 40 minutes
Cooking Time: 7 minutes
Servings: 2

Ingredients:

- 2 avocados, sliced in half and pitted
- ¼ onion, chopped
- 2 tomatoes, chopped
- 1 bell pepper, chopped
- 2 tablespoons cilantro, chopped
- Pepper to taste
- 4 eggs

Method:

1. Scoop out the flesh of the avocado and chop.
2. Place in a bowl.
3. Stir in the rest of the ingredients except.
4. Refrigerate for 30 minutes.
5. Crack egg on top of avocado shell.
6. Preheat your air fryer to 350 degrees F.
7. Air fry for 7 minutes.
8. Top with avocado salsa.

Serving Suggestions: Sprinkle with dried herbs before serving.

Preparation & Cooking Tips: Drizzle salsa with lime juice.

Breakfast Sandwich

Preparation Time: 5 minutes
Cooking Time: 7 minutes
Servings: 1

Ingredients:

- 1 frozen breakfast

Method:

1. Air fry sandwich at 340 degrees F for 7 minutes.

Serving Suggestions: Air fry longer to make the bread crispier.

Preparation & Cooking Tips: Choose sandwich with lean meat and whole grain bread.

Tex-Mex Hash Browns

Preparation Time: 15 minutes
Cooking Time: 30 minutes
Servings: 4

Ingredients:

- 1 ½ lb. potatoes, sliced into cubes
- 1 tablespoon olive oil
- Pepper to taste
- 1 onion, chopped
- 1 red bell pepper, chopped
- 1 jalapeno, sliced into rings
- 1 teaspoon oil
- ½ teaspoon ground cumin
- ½ teaspoon taco seasoning mix

Method:

1. Preheat your air fryer to 320 degrees F.
2. Toss potatoes in 1 tablespoon oil.
3. Season with pepper.
4. Transfer to the air fryer basket.
5. Air fry for 20 minutes, shaking twice during cooking.
6. Combine remaining ingredients in a bowl.
7. Add to the air fryer.
8. Mix well.
9. Cook at 356 degrees F for 10 minutes.

Serving Suggestions: Serve with hot sauce.

Preparation & Cooking Tips: Use habanero if you like your hash browns spicier.

Breakfast Potatoes

Preparation Time: 5 minutes
Cooking Time: 15 minutes
Servings: 2

Ingredients:

- 5 potatoes, sliced into cubes
- 1 tablespoon oil
- ½ teaspoon garlic powder
- ¼ teaspoon pepper
- ½ teaspoon smoked paprika

Method:

1. Preheat your air fryer at 400 degrees F for 5 minutes.
2. Toss potatoes in oil.
3. Season with garlic powder, pepper and paprika.
4. Add potatoes to the air fryer basket.
5. Cook in the air fryer for 15 minutes.

Serving Suggestions: Garnish with chopped parsley.

Preparation & Cooking Tips: Use Yukon Gold potatoes.

Breakfast Frittata

Preparation Time: 15 minutes
Cooking Time: 20 minutes
Servings: 2

Ingredients:

- 1 onion, chopped
- 2 tablespoons red bell pepper, chopped
- ¼ lb. breakfast turkey sausage, cooked and crumbled
- 3 eggs, beaten
- Pinch cayenne pepper

Method:

1. Mix all the ingredients in a bowl.
2. Pour into a small baking pan.
3. Add baking pan to the air fryer basket.
4. Cook in the air fryer for 20 minutes.

Serving Suggestions: Garnish with green onion.

Preparation & Cooking Tips: Omit cayenne pepper if you don't like your breakfast spicy.

Breakfast Stuffed Biscuits

Preparation Time: 35 minutes
Cooking Time: 30 minutes
Servings: 10

Ingredients:

- 1 tablespoon vegetable oil
- ¼ lb. turkey sausage
- 2 eggs, beaten
- Pepper to taste
- 10 oz. refrigerated biscuits
- Cooking spray

Method:

1. In a pan over medium heat, pour the oil and cook sausage for 5 minutes.
2. Transfer to a bowl and set aside.
3. Cook eggs in the pan and season with pepper.
4. Add eggs to the bowl with sausage.
5. Arrange biscuit dough in the air fryer.
6. Top each with the egg and sausage mixture.
7. Fold up and seal.
8. Spray with oil.
9. Cook in the air fryer at 325 degrees F for 8 minutes.
10. Flip and cook for another 7 minutes.

Serving Suggestions: Let cool before serving.

Preparation & Cooking Tips: Line the air fryer with parchment paper before cooking.

Breakfast Omelette

Preparation Time: 5 minutes
Cooking Time: 10 minutes
Servings: 2

Ingredients:

- 2 eggs, beaten
- 1 stalk green onion, chopped
- ½ cup mushrooms, sliced
- 1 red bell pepper, diced
- 1 teaspoon herb seasoning

Method:

1. Beat eggs in a bowl.
2. Stir in the rest of the ingredients.
3. Pour egg mixture into a small baking pan.
4. Add pan to the air fryer basket.
5. Cook in the air fryer basket at 350 degrees F for 10 minutes.

Serving Suggestions: Garnish with additional chopped green onions.

Preparation & Cooking Tips: You can add more vegetables to the mixture if you like.

Breakfast Tofu

Preparation Time: 40 minutes
Cooking Time: 20 minutes
Servings: 4

Ingredients:

- 2 teaspoons toasted sesame oil
- 1 teaspoon rice vinegar
- 2 tablespoons reduced-sodium soy sauce
- ½ teaspoon onion powder
- 1 teaspoon garlic powder
- 1 block tofu, sliced into cubes
- 1 tablespoon potato starch

Method:

1. In a bowl, combine all ingredients except tofu and potato starch.
2. Mix well.
3. Add tofu to the bowl.
4. Marinate for 30 minutes.
5. Coat tofu with the potato starch.
6. Add tofu to the air fryer basket.
7. Air fry at 370 degrees F for 20 minutes, shaking halfway through.

Serving Suggestions: Serve with potato hash.

Preparation & Cooking Tips: You can also marinate longer for 2 hours but cover and refrigerate.

Sweet Potato Hash

Preparation Time: 10 minutes
Cooking Time: 15 minutes
Servings: 6

Ingredients:

- 2 sweet potatoes, sliced into cubes
- 2 tablespoons olive oil
- 1 tablespoon paprika
- 1 teaspoon dried dill weed
- Pepper to taste

Method:

1. Preheat your air fryer to 400 degrees F.
2. Combine all ingredients in a bowl.
3. Transfer to your air fryer.
4. Cook for 15 minutes, stirring every 5 minutes.

Serving Suggestions: Serve with whole wheat bread.

Preparation & Cooking Tips: You can also use smoked paprika for this recipe.

Chapter 5: Meat & Poultry

Chicken Thighs

Preparation Time: 15 minutes

Cooking Time: 20 minutes

Servings: 4

Ingredients:

- 4 chicken thigh fillets
- 2 teaspoons olive oil
- 1 teaspoon garlic powder
- 1 teaspoon paprika
- Pepper to taste

Method:

1. Preheat your air fryer to 400 degrees F.
2. Coat chicken with oil.
3. Sprinkle both sides of chicken with garlic powder, paprika and pepper.
4. Air fry for 20 minutes.

Serving Suggestions: Serve with ketchup or gravy.

Preparation & Cooking Tips: Use smoked paprika if available.

Beef Tips

Preparation Time: 10 minutes

Cooking Time: 12 minutes

Servings: 4

Ingredients:

- 2 teaspoons onion powder
- 1 teaspoon garlic powder
- 2 teaspoons rosemary, chopped
- 1 teaspoon paprika
- 2 tablespoons low-sodium coconut amino
- Pepper to taste
- 1 lb. steak, sliced into strips

Method:

1. Mix all spices and seasoning in a bowl.
2. Stir in steak strips.
3. Marinate for 10 minutes.
4. Add to the air fryer basket.
5. Cook at 380 degrees F for 12 minutes, shaking once or twice halfway through the cooking.

Serving Suggestions: Serve with mashed potatoes.

Preparation & Cooking Tips: You can replace fresh rosemary with 1 teaspoon dried rosemary.

Meatloaf

Preparation Time: 10 minutes
Cooking Time: 30 minutes
Servings: 4

Ingredients:

- 1 lb. lean ground beef
- 3 tablespoons breadcrumbs
- 1 onion, chopped
- 1 tablespoon fresh thyme, chopped
- Garlic powder to taste
- Pepper to taste
- 2 mushrooms, chopped
- 1 tablespoon olive oil

Method:

1. Preheat your air fryer to 392 degrees F.
2. Combine all ingredients in a bowl.
3. Press mixture into a small loaf pan.
4. Add pan to the air fryer basket.
5. Cook for 30 minutes.

Serving Suggestions: Let rest for 15 minutes before slicing and serving.

Preparation & Cooking Tips: You can also use lean ground chicken or turkey for this recipe.

Crispy Chicken Tenderloin

Preparation Time: 15 minutes
Cooking Time: 15 minutes
Servings: 4

Ingredients:

- 1 egg, beaten
- 8 chicken tenderloin
- 2 tablespoons avocado oil
- ½ cup breadcrumbs

Method:

1. Preheat your air fryer to 350 degrees F.
2. Dip chicken in egg.
3. Mix oil and breadcrumbs.
4. Coat chicken with this mixture.
5. Add to the air fryer basket.
6. Cook for 15 minutes.

Serving Suggestions: Serve with gravy.

Preparation & Cooking Tips: For large cuts, cook for 20 minutes.

Chicken Taquitos

Preparation Time: 15 minutes

Cooking Time: 20 minutes

Servings: 6

Ingredients:

- 1 teaspoon vegetable oil
- 1 onion, chopped
- 2 tablespoon green chili, chopped
- 1 clove garlic, minced
- 1 cup chicken, cooked
- 2 tablespoons hot sauce
- ½ cup reduced-sodium cheese blend
- Pepper to taste
- Corn tortillas, warmed
- Cooking spray

Method:

1. Pour into a pan over medium heat.
2. Cook onion, green chili and garlic for 5 minutes, stirring often.
3. Stir in the rest of the ingredients except tortillas.
4. Cook for 3 minutes.
5. Add mixture on top of the tortillas.
6. Roll up the tortillas.
7. Preheat your air fryer to 400 degrees F.
8. Place in the air fryer basket.
9. Cook for 10 minutes.

Serving Suggestions: Drizzle with more hot sauce before serving.

Preparation & Cooking Tips: Leftover rotisserie chicken can also be used.

Steak with Asparagus

Preparation Time: 20 minutes
Cooking Time: 10 minutes
Servings: 4

Ingredients:

Steak

- 1 lb. steak, fat trimmed and sliced into cubes
- 1 teaspoon oil
- ½ teaspoon onion powder
- ½ garlic powder
- 1/8 teaspoon cayenne pepper
- 1 teaspoon reduced sodium steak seasoning
- Pepper to taste

Asparagus

- 1 lb. asparagus, trimmed
- 1 teaspoon oil
- Garlic powder to taste

Method:

1. Preheat your air fryer to 400 degrees F.
2. Toss steak cubes in oil and seasoning.
3. Cover and marinate for 10 minutes.
4. Add to the air fryer basket.
5. Cook for 5 minutes.
6. Coat asparagus with oil and garlic powder.
7. Add to the air fryer basket.
8. Cook for 5 minutes.

Serving Suggestions: Serve with low-sodium gravy.

Preparation & Cooking Tips: Omit cayenne pepper if you don't like your dish spicy.

Meatball

Preparation Time: 15 minutes
Cooking Time: 15 minutes
Servings: 4

Ingredients:

- Cooking spray
- 2 lb. lean ground beef
- ¼ cup onion, minced
- 2 cloves garlic, minced
- 2 tablespoons parsley, chopped
- Pepper to taste
- ½ teaspoon red pepper flakes
- 1 teaspoon Italian seasoning

Method:

1. Spray your air fryer basket with oil.
2. In a bowl, mix the remaining ingredients.
3. Form meatballs from the mixture.
4. Add to the air fryer basket.
5. Cook for 15 minutes, shaking once or twice.

Serving Suggestions: Serve with tomato sauce and whole wheat pasta.

Preparation & Cooking Tips: Do not overcrowd the air fryer basket. Cook in batches if necessary.

Parmesan Chicken

Preparation Time: 10 minutes
Cooking Time: 10 minutes
Servings: 4

Ingredients:

- 4 chicken breast fillets
- 2 teaspoons garlic powder
- 2 teaspoons Italian seasoning
- Pepper to taste
- ¼ cup Parmesan cheese
- ½ cup breadcrumbs
- 1 cup breadcrumbs
- 2 eggs, beaten
- Cooking spray

Method:

1. Flatten chicken breast with meat mallet.
2. Season with garlic powder, Italian seasoning and pepper.
3. Mix almond flour and Parmesan cheese in a bowl.
4. Add eggs to another bowl.
5. Dip chicken fillet in the eggs and then in the flour.
6. Spray with oil.
7. Place in the air fryer.
8. Cook at 350 degrees F for 10 minutes per side.

Serving Suggestions: Serve with marinara sauce.

Preparation & Cooking Tips: Use freshly grated Parmesan cheese.

Steak & Mushrooms

Preparation Time: 10 minutes
Cooking Time: 15 minutes
Servings: 4

Ingredients:

- 2 tablespoons olive oil
- 8 oz. mushrooms, sliced
- ½ teaspoon garlic powder
- 1 lb. steak, sliced into cubes
- 1 teaspoon (5 ml) Worcestershire sauce
- Pepper to taste

Method:

1. Preheat your air fryer to 400 degrees F.
2. Combine all ingredients in a bowl.
3. Transfer to the air fryer basket.
4. Cook for 15 minutes, shaking the basket twice.

Serving Suggestions: Sprinkle with dried chili flakes.

Preparation & Cooking Tips: Cook for 5 more minutes if you want your steak well done.

Turkey Breast Tenderloin

Preparation Time: 10 minutes

Cooking Time: 25 minutes

Servings: 4

Ingredients:

- 1 turkey breast tenderloin, sliced
- 1 teaspoon paprika
- ½ teaspoon thyme
- ½ teaspoon sage
- Pepper to taste

Method:

1. Preheat your air fryer to 350 degrees F.
2. Sprinkle both sides of turkey with paprika, thyme, sage and pepper.
3. Cook for 15 minutes.
4. Flip and cook for another 10 minutes.

Serving Suggestions: Serve with dip of choice.

Preparation & Cooking Tips: You can also use chicken breast for this recipe.

Crispy Chicken Tenders

Preparation Time: 15 minutes
Cooking Time: 10 minutes
Servings: 4

Ingredients:

- 1 lb. chicken tenders
- 1 tablespoon olive oil

Breading

- ¼ cup breadcrumbs
- 1 teaspoon paprika
- Pepper to taste
- ¼ teaspoon garlic powder
- ¼ teaspoon onion powder
- Pinch cayenne pepper

Method:

1. Preheat your air fryer to 390 degrees F.
2. Coat chicken with olive oil.
3. In a bowl, combine breading ingredients.
4. Cover chicken with breading.
5. Place in the air fryer basket.
6. Cook for 3 to 5 minutes.
7. Flip and cook for another 3 minutes.

Serving Suggestions: Serve with ketchup or hot sauce.

Preparation & Cooking Tips: Coat the chicken with breading ahead of time and freeze. Cook in the air fryer when ready to serve.

Southern Style Chicken

Preparation Time: 20 minutes
Cooking Time: 20 minutes
Servings: 6

Ingredients:

- 2 lb. chicken legs
- 1 ½ teaspoons onion powder
- 2 teaspoons garlic powder
- 2 teaspoons paprika
- 1 teaspoon Italian Seasoning
- Pepper to taste
- 1 cup flour
- 1 tablespoon olive oil
- ¼ cup water
- 2 tablespoons milk
- 1 tablespoon hot sauce
- Cooking spray

Method:

1. Season chicken with onion powder, garlic powder, paprika, Italian seasoning and pepper.
2. Dredge with flour.
3. In a bowl, mix olive oil, water, milk and hot sauce.
4. Dip chicken in the olive oil mixture.
5. Spray with oil.
6. Add to air fryer basket.
7. Air fry at 350 degrees F for 20 minutes, flipping once.

Serving Suggestions: Serve immediately.

Preparation & Cooking Tips: You can also use chicken thighs or breast fillets for this recipe.

Chicken Breast

Preparation Time: 10 minutes
Cooking Time: 20 minutes
Servings: 4

Ingredients:

- 4 chicken breast fillets
- ½ teaspoon dried oregano
- ½ teaspoon garlic powder
- Pepper to taste
- Cooking spray

Method:

1. Season chicken with oregano, garlic powder and pepper.
2. Spray with oil.
3. Place in the air fryer basket.
4. Air fry at 360 degrees F for 10 minutes per side.

Serving Suggestions: Serve with dip of choice.

Preparation & Cooking Tips: Cook in batches to brown chicken evenly.

Roasted Whole Chicken

Preparation Time: 15 minutes

Cooking Time: 1 hour

Servings: 5

Ingredients:

- 1 whole chicken
- ½ onion
- ½ lemon
- 4 sprigs fresh rosemary
- 4 sprigs fresh thyme
- Cooking spray
- 2 teaspoons onion powder
- 2 teaspoons garlic powder
- Pinch ground thyme
- Pepper to taste

Method:

1. Stuff chicken with onion, lemon and herbs.
2. Spray outside with oil.
3. Sprinkle onion powder, garlic powder, thyme and pepper all over the chicken.
4. Add chicken to the air fryer basket.
5. Cook at 330 degrees F for 30 minutes.
6. Flip chicken and cook for another 30 minutes.

Serving Suggestions: Let rest for 15 minutes before serving.

Preparation & Cooking Tips: Buy pre-prepared whole chicken so you don't have to clean and remove giblets anymore.

Chicken Katsu

Preparation Time: 20 minutes
Cooking Time: 20 minutes
Servings: 4

Ingredients:

Katsu Sauce

- 2 tablespoons soy sauce
- ½ cup ketchup
- 1 tablespoon sherry
- 1 tablespoon brown sugar
- 2 teaspoons Worcestershire sauce
- 1 teaspoon garlic, minced

Chicken

- 1 lb. chicken breast fillet, sliced
- Pepper to taste
- Pinch garlic powder
- 1 tablespoon olive oil
- 1 ½ cups breadcrumbs
- Cooking spray

Method:

1. Combine katsu sauce ingredients in a bowl. Set aside.
2. Preheat your air fryer to 350 degrees F.
3. Season chicken with pepper.
4. Coat chicken with oil and dredge with breadcrumbs.
5. Place in the air fryer basket.
6. Spray with oil.
7. Cook in the air fryer for 10 minutes per side.
8. Serve with sauce.

Serving Suggestions: Drizzle with katsu sauce and garnish with sesame seeds.

Preparation & Cooking Tips: Cook longer for larger cuts.

Chapter 6: Fish & Seafood

Crumbed Fish

Preparation Time: 10 minutes

Cooking Time: 15 minutes

Servings: 4

Ingredients:

- ¼ cup olive oil
- 1 cup dry breadcrumbs
- 4 white fish fillets
- Pepper to taste

Method:

1. Preheat your air fryer to 350 degrees F.
2. Sprinkle both sides of fish with pepper.
3. Combine oil and breadcrumbs in a bowl.
4. Dip the fish into the mixture.
5. Press breadcrumbs to adhere.
6. Place fish in the air fryer.
7. Cook for 15 minutes.

Serving Suggestions: Add lemon slices on top before serving.

Preparation & Cooking Tips: Pat fish dry with paper towels before sprinkling with seasoning.

Fish Patties

Preparation Time: 5 minutes
Cooking Time: 7 minutes
Servings: 2

Ingredients:

- 8 oz. white fish fillet, flaked
- Garlic powder to taste
- 1 teaspoon lemon juice

Method:

1. Preheat your air fryer to 390 degrees F.
2. Combine all the ingredients.
3. Form patties from the mixture.
4. Place fish patties in the air fryer.
5. Cook for 7 minutes.

Serving Suggestions: Serve with hot sauce.

Preparation & Cooking Tips: You can also use salmon for this recipe.

Cajun Salmon

Preparation Time: 10 minutes

Cooking Time: 10 minutes

Servings: 2

Ingredients:

- 2 salmon fillets
- Cooking spray
- 1 tablespoon Cajun seasoning
- 1 tablespoon honey

Method:

1. Preheat your air fryer to 390 degrees F.
2. Spray both sides of fish with oil.
3. Sprinkle with Cajun seasoning.
4. Spray air fryer basket with oil.
5. Add salmon to the air fryer basket.
6. Air fry for 10 minutes.

Serving Suggestions: Serve with dip of choice.

Preparation & Cooking Tips: You can also use maple syrup if honey is not available.

Lime & Chili Salmon

Preparation Time: 10 minutes
Cooking Time: 8 minutes
Servings: 2

Ingredients:

- 1 lb. salmon
- 1 tablespoon lime juice
- ½ teaspoon pepper
- ½ teaspoon chili powder
- 4 lime slices

Method:

1. Drizzle salmon with lime juice.
2. Sprinkle both sides with pepper and chili powder.
3. Add salmon to the air fryer.
4. Place lime slices on top of salmon.
5. Air fry at 375 degrees F for 8 minutes.

Serving Suggestions: Garnish with chopped parsley.

Preparation & Cooking Tips: Fresh salmon is best used for this recipe.

Mexican Fish

Preparation Time: 20 minutes
Cooking Time: 10 minutes
Servings: 2

Ingredients:

- 4 fish fillets
- 2 teaspoons Mexican oregano
- 4 teaspoons cumin
- 4 teaspoons chili powder
- Pepper to taste
- Cooking spray

Method:

1. Preheat your air fryer to 400 degrees F.
2. Spray fish with oil.
3. Season both sides of fish with spices and pepper.
4. Place fish in the air fryer basket.
5. Cook for 5 minutes.
6. Flip and cook for another 5 minutes.

Serving Suggestions: Drizzle with lime juice before serving.

Preparation & Cooking Tips: Cook fish in batches.

Popcorn Shrimp

Preparation Time: 15 minutes
Cooking Time: 10 minutes
Servings: 4

Ingredients:

- ½ teaspoon onion powder
- ½ teaspoon garlic powder
- ½ teaspoon paprika
- ¼ teaspoon ground mustard
- ⅛ teaspoon dried sage
- ⅛ teaspoon ground thyme
- ⅛ teaspoon dried oregano
- ⅛ teaspoon dried basil
- Pepper to taste
- 3 tablespoons cornstarch
- 1 lb. shrimp, peeled and deveined
- Cooking spray

Method:

1. Combine all ingredients except shrimp in a bowl.
2. Coat shrimp with the mixture.
3. Spray air fryer basket with oil.
4. Preheat your air fryer to 390 degrees F.
5. Add shrimp inside.
6. Air fry for 4 minutes.
7. Shake the basket.
8. Cook for another 5 minutes.

Serving Suggestions: Serve popcorn shrimp immediately.

Preparation & Cooking Tips: After breading, let shrimp rest for 10 minutes before cooking.

Lemon Pepper Shrimp

Preparation Time: 10 minutes
Cooking Time: 10 minutes
Servings: 2

Ingredients:

- 1 tablespoon lemon juice
- 1 tablespoon olive oil
- 1 teaspoon lemon pepper
- ¼ teaspoon garlic powder
- ¼ teaspoon paprika
- 12 oz. shrimp, peeled and deveined

Method:

1. Preheat your air fryer to 400 degrees F.
2. Mix lemon juice, olive oil, lemon pepper, garlic powder and paprika in a bowl.
3. Stir in shrimp and coat evenly with the mixture.
4. Add to the air fryer.
5. Cook for 8 minutes.

Serving Suggestions: Garnish with lemon slices.

Preparation & Cooking Tips: You can also use frozen shrimp for this recipe and extend cooking time to 10 minutes.

Salmon Cakes

Preparation Time: 30 minutes

Cooking Time: 10 minutes

Servings: 4

Ingredients:

- Cooking spray
- 1 lb. salmon fillet, flaked
- ¼ cup almond flour
- 2 teaspoons Old Bay seasoning
- 1 green onion, chopped

Method:

1. Preheat your air fryer to 390 degrees F.
2. Spray your air fryer basket with oil.
3. In a bowl, combine the remaining ingredients.
4. Form patties from the mixture.
5. Spray both sides of patties with oil.
6. Air fry for 8 minutes.

Serving Suggestions: Serve with green salad.

Preparation & Cooking Tips: Refrigerate patties for 15 minutes before cooking.

Shrimp Bang Bang

Preparation Time: 15 minutes
Cooking Time: 25 minutes
Servings: 4

Ingredients:

- 1 tablespoon hot sauce
- ¼ cup sweet chili sauce
- ½ cup light mayonnaise
- ¼ cup all-purpose flour
- 1 cup breadcrumbs
- 1 lb. shrimp, peeled and deveined

Method:

1. Set your air fryer to 400 degrees F.
2. In a bowl, mix the hot sauce, chili sauce and mayo.
3. Divide mixture into 2 bowls.
4. Reserve 1 bowl for dipping later.
5. Coat the shrimp with flour.
6. Dip in mayo mixture.
7. Dredge with breadcrumbs.
8. Air fry for 12 minutes, shaking once halfway through.

Serving Suggestions: Serve on top of lettuce leaves.

Preparation & Cooking Tips: Do not overcrowd the air fryer. Cook in batches if necessary.

Coconut Shrimp

Preparation Time: 30 minutes

Cooking Time: 10 minutes

Servings: 6

Ingredients:

- Pepper to taste
- ½ cup all-purpose flour
- 2 eggs, beaten
- ½ cup breadcrumbs
- ¼ cup coconut flakes (unsweetened)
- 12 oz. shrimp, peeled and deveined
- Cooking spray
- ¼ cup honey
- ¼ cup lime juice
- 1 chili pepper, sliced thinly

Method:

1. Add pepper and flour to a bowl. Mix.
2. In another bowl, place the beaten eggs.
3. In the third bowl, combine breadcrumbs and coconut flakes.
4. Dip shrimp in the first, second and third bowls.
5. Spray each with oil.
6. Preheat your air fryer to 400 degrees F.
7. Add shrimp to the air fryer.
8. Cook for 3 minutes per side.
9. Mix the remaining ingredients.
10. Serve shrimp with honey lime dip.

Serving Suggestions: Garnish with chopped cilantro.

Preparation & Cooking Tips: If you'll use frozen shrimp for this recipe, add 2 to 3 minutes cooking time.

Crispy Garlic Shrimp

Preparation Time: 10 minutes
Cooking Time: 10 minutes
Servings: 4

Ingredients:

- 1 lb. shrimp, peeled and deveined
- 2 teaspoons garlic powder
- Pepper to taste
- ¼ cup flour
- Cooking spray

Method:

1. Season shrimp with garlic powder and pepper.
2. Coat with flour.
3. Spray your air fryer basket with oil.
4. Add shrimp to the air fryer basket.
5. Cook at 400 degrees F for 10 minutes, shaking once halfway through.

Serving Suggestions: Garnish with chopped parsley.

Preparation & Cooking Tips: Cook shrimp in batches to avoid overcrowding.

Scallops

Preparation Time: 20 minutes
Cooking Time: 10 minutes
Servings: 2

Ingredients:

- 8 scallops
- Pepper to taste
- Cooking spray
- ¼ cup olive oil
- 1 teaspoon lemon zest
- ½ teaspoon garlic, chopped
- 2 teaspoons capers, chopped
- 2 tablespoons parsley, chopped

Method:

1. Season scallops with pepper.
2. Spray air fryer basket with oil.
3. Spray scallops with oil.
4. Cook in the air fryer at 400 degrees F for 6 minutes.
5. In a bowl, mix the remaining ingredients.
6. Drizzle mixture over the scallops and serve.

Serving Suggestions: Garnish with chopped parsley.

Preparation & Cooking Tips: Pat scallops dry before seasoning and cooking.

Crispy Shrimp

Preparation Time: 15 minutes

Cooking Time: 3 minutes

Servings: 4

Ingredients:

- 1 lb. shrimp, peeled and deveined
- ½ cup fish breading mix
- Cooking spray

Method:

1. Preheat your air fryer to 390 degrees F.
2. Spray shrimp with oil.
3. Coat with the breading mix.
4. Spray air fryer basket with oil.
5. Add shrimp to air fryer basket.
6. Cook for 3 minutes.

Serving Suggestions: Garnish with chopped parsley.

Preparation & Cooking Tips: After breading the shrimp, let rest for 10 minutes before cooking.

Coconut Crusted Fish Strips

Preparation Time: 2 hours and 20 minutes
Cooking Time: 12 minutes
Servings: 4

Ingredients:

Marinade

- 1 tablespoon soy sauce
- 1 teaspoon ground ginger
- ½ cup coconut milk
- 2 tablespoons maple syrup
- ½ cup pineapple juice
- 2 teaspoons hot sauce

Fish

- 1 lb. fish fillet, sliced into strips
- Pepper to taste
- 1 cup breadcrumbs
- 1 cup coconut flakes (unsweetened)
- Cooking spray

Method:

1. Mix marinade ingredients in a bowl.
2. Stir in fish strips.
3. Cover and refrigerate for 2 hours.
4. Preheat your air fryer to 375 degrees F.
5. In a bowl, mix pepper, breadcrumbs and coconut flakes.
6. Dip fish strips in the breadcrumb mixture.
7. Spray your air fryer basket with oil.
8. Add fish strips to the air fryer basket.
9. Air fry for 6 minutes per side.

Serving Suggestions: Serve with cooked brown rice.

Preparation & Cooking Tips: You can also marinate fish overnight.

Fish Tacos

Preparation Time: 15 minutes
Cooking Time: 20 minutes
Servings: 4

Ingredients:

- Cooking spray
- 1 tablespoon olive oil
- 4 cups cabbage slaw
- 1 tablespoon apple cider vinegar
- 1 tablespoon lime juice
- Pinch cayenne pepper
- Pepper to taste
- 2 tablespoons taco seasoning mix
- ¼ cup all-purpose flour
- 1 lb. cod fillet, sliced into cubes
- 4 corn tortillas

Method:

1. Preheat your air fryer to 400 degrees F.
2. Spray your air fryer basket with oil.
3. In a bowl, mix the olive oil, cabbage slaw, vinegar, lime juice, cayenne pepper and pepper.
4. In another bowl, mix the taco seasoning and flour.
5. Coat the fish cubes with the taco seasoning mixture.
6. Add these to the air fryer basket.
7. Air fry for 10 minutes, shaking halfway through.
8. Top the corn tortillas with the fish and cabbage slaw mixture and roll them up.

Serving Suggestions: Serve with hot sauce.

Preparation & Cooking Tips: You can also air fry the slaw for 5 minutes to caramelize.

Chapter 7: Vegetables

Mushroom Pizza

Preparation Time: 5 minutes
Cooking Time: 10 minutes
Servings: 2

Ingredients:

- 2 tablespoons olive oil
- 2 mushrooms caps
- 1 teaspoon Italian seasoning
- 6 tablespoons pizza sauce
- 2 tablespoons black olives, sliced

Method:

1. Preheat your air fryer to 350 degrees F.
2. Drizzle half of oil over mushrooms.
3. Season with Italian seasoning.
4. Place in the air fryer basket.
5. Cook for 3 minutes.
6. Flip and cook for another 3 minutes.
7. Pour pizza sauce into the mushrooms.
8. Top with olives.
9. Cook for 3 minutes.

Serving Suggestions: Sprinkle with dried herbs before serving.

Preparation & Cooking Tips: You can also sprinkle with a little Parmesan cheese on top.

Garlic Baby Potatoes

Preparation Time: 10 minutes
Cooking Time: 25 minutes
Servings: 4

Ingredients:

- 1 lb. baby potatoes, sliced in half
- 1 tablespoon avocado oil
- ½ teaspoon granulated garlic
- 1 tablespoon parsley, chopped

Method:

1. Preheat your air fryer to 350 degrees F.
2. Toss potatoes in oil and garlic.
3. Sprinkle with half of parsley.
4. Add to the air fryer basket.
5. Cook for 25 minutes, shaking every 5 or 7 minutes.

Serving Suggestions: Garnish with remaining parsley.

Preparation & Cooking Tips: You can also use regular sized potatoes for this recipe and simply slice into wedges before cooking.

Stuffed Peppers

Preparation Time: 5 minutes

Cooking Time: 8 minutes

Servings: 4

Ingredients:

- Cooking spray
- 1 tablespoon olive oil
- ¾ cup reduced-sodium marinara sauce
- 1 cup cooked brown rice
- 3 tablespoons parsley, chopped
- ¼ cup breadcrumbs
- Pepper to taste
- 4 large red bell peppers, tops sliced off

Method:

1. Spray air fryer basket with oil.
2. Mix the olive oil, marinara sauce, rice, parsley, breadcrumbs and pepper in a bowl.
3. Stuff peppers with the mixture.
4. Add peppers to the air fryer basket.
5. Air fry at 350 degrees F for 8 minutes.

Serving Suggestions: Garnish with chopped parsley.

Preparation & Cooking Tips: Toast breadcrumbs before adding to the mixture.

Garlic Cauliflower

Preparation Time: 10 minutes

Cooking Time: 15 minutes

Servings: 2

Ingredients:

- 4 cups cauliflower florets
- 1 tablespoon olive oil
- 1 teaspoon smoked paprika
- 3 cloves garlic, minced

Method:

1. Preheat your air fryer to 400 degrees F.
2. Coat the cauliflower florets with oil.
3. Sprinkle with paprika and garlic.
4. Air fry for 15 minutes, shaking every 5 minutes.

Serving Suggestions: Serve with sweet chili sauce.

Preparation & Cooking Tips: Do not overcrowd the air fryer. Cook in batches if necessary.

Maple Brussels Sprouts

Preparation Time: 5 minutes
Cooking Time: 10 minutes
Servings: 4

Ingredients:

- 1 tablespoon olive oil
- 1 tablespoons maple syrup
- Pepper to taste
- 1 lb. Brussels sprouts, trimmed and sliced in half

Method:

1. Preheat your air fryer to 400 degrees F.
2. Mix oil, maple syrup and pepper.
3. Toss Brussels sprouts in the mixture.
4. Transfer to the air fryer basket.
5. Air fry 10 minutes, shaking once or twice.

Serving Suggestions: Serve with mustard.

Zucchini Marinara

Preparation Time: 10 minutes
Cooking Time: 15 minutes
Servings: 4

Ingredients:

- 2 zucchinis, sliced in half lengthwise
- 4 tablespoons herbed tomato sauce
- 1 tablespoon olive oil
- 1 tablespoon fresh parsley, chopped
- 2 tablespoons breadcrumbs
- Pepper to taste

Method:

1. Preheat your air fryer to 350 degrees F.
2. Add zucchinis to a baking pan or plate.
3. In a bowl, mix remaining ingredients.
4. Pour mixture on top of zucchini boats.
5. Add to the air fryer basket.
6. Air fry for 15 minutes.

Serving Suggestions: Sprinkle with dried herbs before serving.

Preparation & Cooking Tips: You can also add a little Parmesan cheese into the mixture.

Crispy Eggplant Parmesan

Preparation Time: 15 minutes
Cooking Time: 20 minutes
Servings: 4

Ingredients:

- ¼ cup flour
- 2 eggs, beaten
- ½ cup Italian breadcrumbs
- ¼ cup Parmesan cheese, grated
- 1 teaspoon Italian seasoning
- ½ teaspoon dried basil
- ½ teaspoon onion powder
- 1 teaspoon garlic powder
- Pepper to taste
- 1 eggplant, sliced into rounds
- 1 cup low-sodium marinara sauce

Method:

1. Add flour to a bowl.
2. Add eggs to another bowl.
3. In the third bowl, mix the remaining ingredients except eggplant and marinara sauce.
4. Dip eggplant slices in the first, second and third bowls.
5. Preheat your air fryer to 370 degrees F.
6. Add eggplant to the air fryer basket.
7. Cook for 10 minutes.
8. Serve with marinara sauce.

Serving Suggestions: Sprinkle with chopped parsley before serving.

Preparation & Cooking Tips: You can also use this recipe for zucchini strips.

Spicy Green Beans

Preparation Time: 15 minutes
Cooking Time: 12 minutes
Servings: 4

Ingredients:

- 12 oz. green beans, trimmed and sliced
- 1 tablespoon sesame oil
- 1 teaspoon soy sauce
- ½ teaspoon rice wine vinegar
- 1 clove garlic, minced
- ½ teaspoon crushed red pepper

Method:

1. Preheat your air fryer to 400 degrees F.
2. Add green beans to a bowl.
3. In another bowl, mix the remaining ingredients.
4. Pour mixture into the first bowl.
5. Coat green beans with the mixture.
6. Marinate for 5 minutes.
7. Air fry the green beans for 12 minutes, shaking every 4 minutes.

Serving Suggestions: Drizzle with vinegar before serving.

Preparation & Cooking Tips: Cook green beans in 2 batches.

Buffalo Cauliflower

Preparation Time: 10 minutes
Cooking Time: 15 minutes
Servings: 4

Ingredients:

- 2 tablespoons hot sauce
- 1 teaspoon maple syrup
- 2 teaspoons avocado oil
- 1 tablespoon cornstarch
- 6 cups cauliflower florets

Method:

1. Preheat your air fryer to 360 degrees F.
2. Combine all ingredients except cauliflower in a bowl.
3. Mix well.
4. Stir in cauliflower.
5. Add to the air fryer basket.
6. Cook for 15 minutes, shaking every 5 minutes.

Serving Suggestions: Sprinkle with chopped parsley.

Preparation & Cooking Tips: You can refrigerate this for up to 4 days.

Stuffed Mushrooms

Preparation Time: 20 minutes
Cooking Time: 10 minutes
Servings: 6

Ingredients:

- 4 oz. cream cheese
- 2 scallions, chopped
- ¼ teaspoon ground paprika
- Pepper to taste
- 16 oz. large mushrooms caps
- Cooking spray

Method:

1. Preheat your air fryer to 360 degrees F.
2. Mix cream cheese, scallions, paprika and pepper.
3. Stuff mushrooms with mixture.
4. Spray mushrooms and air fryer basket with oil.
5. Add mushrooms to air fryer basket.
6. Air fry for 8 to 10 minutes.

Serving Suggestions: Garnish with chopped green onions.

Preparation & Cooking Tips: Dry mushrooms with paper towel before seasoning.

Baked Potatoes

Preparation Time: 5 minutes

Cooking Time: 1 hour

Servings: 2

Ingredients:

- 2 large potatoes
- 1 tablespoon peanut oil
- Pepper to taste

Method:

1. Preheat your air fryer to 400 degrees F.
2. Coat potatoes with oil and season with pepper.
3. Add to the air fryer basket.
4. Air fry potatoes for 1 hour.

Serving Suggestions: Serve with sour cream.

Preparation & Cooking Tips: Pierce the potatoes with a fork before air frying.

Brussels Sprouts

Preparation Time: 5 minutes
Cooking Time: 10 minutes
Servings: 2

Ingredients:

- 2 cups Brussels sprouts, sliced in half
- 1 tablespoon olive oil
- 1 tablespoon balsamic vinegar
- Pepper to taste

Method:

1. Toss Brussels sprouts in oil and vinegar.
2. Season with pepper.
3. Air fry at 400 degrees F for 10 minutes, shaking once or twice.

Serving Suggestions: Garnish with chopped chives.

Preparation & Cooking Tips: You can also season with garlic powder.

Honey Roasted Carrots

Preparation Time: 10 minutes
Cooking Time: 10 minutes
Servings: 4

Ingredients:

- 2 tablespoons olive oil, divided
- Pepper to taste
- 1 teaspoon honey
- 1 lb. baby carrots
- 1 tablespoon balsamic glaze

Method:

1. Add 1 tablespoon oil, pepper and honey in a bowl.
2. Coat carrots with this mixture.
3. Add to the air fryer basket.
4. Air fry at 390 degrees F for 10 minutes.
5. Drizzle with balsamic glaze.

Serving Suggestions: Sprinkle with chives.

Preparation & Cooking Tips: Use multi-colored carrots.

Artichoke Hearts

Preparation Time: 10 minutes
Cooking Time: 7 minutes
Servings: 4

Ingredients:

- 14 oz. canned artichoke hearts, drained and sliced into wedges
- 1 tablespoon olive oil
- ½ teaspoon garlic powder
- ¼ teaspoon Italian seasoning
- Pepper to taste

Method:

1. Preheat your air fryer to 390 degrees F.
2. Coat artichokes with oil.
3. Season with garlic power, Italian seasoning and pepper.
4. Add to the air fryer basket.
5. Air fry for 7 minutes, shaking once.

Serving Suggestions: Serve immediately.

Preparation & Cooking Tips: Dry artichoke hearts with paper towel before preparing.

Roasted Okra

Preparation Time: 5 minutes
Cooking Time: 15 minutes
Servings: 1

Ingredients:

- ½ lb. okra, trimmed and sliced
- 1 teaspoon olive oil
- Pepper to taste

Method:

1. Preheat your air fryer to 350 degrees F.
2. Toss okra in oil and pepper.
3. Add to the air fryer basket.
4. Air fry for 5 minutes.
5. Shake and cook for another 5 minutes.
6. Shake once more and cook for 2 minutes.

Serving Suggestions: Serve immediately.

Preparation & Cooking Tips: Arrange okra in a single layer in the air fryer.

Chapter 8: Healthy Snacks

Buffalo Tofu Bites

Preparation Time: 15 minutes
Cooking Time: 15 minutes
Servings: 20

Ingredients:

- 8 oz. tofu, sliced into cubes
- 4 tablespoons cornstarch
- 4 tablespoons rice milk (unsweetened)
- ¼ teaspoon paprika
- ¼ teaspoon garlic powder
- ¼ teaspoon onion powder
- ¾ cup breadcrumbs
- ¼ cup Buffalo sauce

Method:

1. Pat tofu cubes dry with paper towels.
2. Preheat your air fryer to 375 degrees F.
3. Coat tofu cubes with cornstarch.
4. Dip each tofu cube with rice milk.
5. Mix remaining ingredients except Buffalo sauce in a bowl.
6. Dredge tofu cubes with the mixture.
7. Add to the air fryer basket.
8. Air fry for 10 minutes.
9. Shake and cook for another 3 minutes.
10. Coat cooked tofu cubes with Buffalo sauce and serve.

Serving Suggestions: Serve with remaining Buffalo sauce.

Preparation & Cooking Tips: Use extra-firm tofu for this recipe.

Kale Chips

Preparation Time: 15 minutes
Cooking Time: 15 minutes
Servings: 4

Ingredients:

- 4 cups kale
- 2 cloves garlic, minced
- 1 cup cashews
- 1 tablespoon tamari sauce
- 2 tablespoons water
- ¼ cup nutritional yeast

Method:

1. Add kale leaves to a bowl.
2. Add remaining ingredients to a food processor.
3. Pulse until well blended.
4. Add mixture to the bowl with kale.
5. Coat evenly with the mixture.
6. Add to the air fryer basket.
7. Air fry at 350 degrees F for 15 minutes.

Serving Suggestions: Serve immediately.

Preparation & Cooking Tips: Soak cashews in water overnight before preparing.

Mac & Cheese Bites

Preparation Time: 3 hours and 15 minutes
Cooking Time: 15 minutes
Servings: 4

Ingredients:

- 7 oz. mac and cheese dinner mix, cooked according to package directions
- ¼ cup almond milk
- Cooking spray
- 1 teaspoon garlic powder
- 1 cup breadcrumbs

Method:

1. Add cooked mac and cheese to a pot over medium heat.
2. Stir in the milk.
3. Cook while stirring for 5 minutes.
4. Transfer to a small baking pan.
5. Cover and refrigerate for 2 hours.
6. Scoop mixture and form into balls.
7. Freeze balls for 1 hour.
8. Preheat your air fryer to 350 degrees F.
9. Spray air fryer with oil.
10. Spray balls with oil and season with garlic powder.
11. Dredge with breadcrumbs.
12. Place in the air fryer basket.
13. Air fry for 6 minutes.
14. Turn and cook for another 4 minutes.

Serving Suggestions: Serve with marinara dipping sauce.

Preparation & Cooking Tips: Cook until golden and crispy.

Garlic Zucchini Chips

Preparation Time: 10 minutes
Cooking Time: 25 minutes
Servings: 4

Ingredients:

- Cooking spray
- 1 zucchini, sliced thinly into rounds
- 1 tablespoon garlic powder
- 1 cup breadcrumbs

Method:

1. Preheat your air fryer to 350 degrees F.
2. Spray zucchini with oil.
3. Sprinkle with garlic powder and dredge with breadcrumbs.
4. Add to the air fryer basket.
5. Air fry for 10 minutes.
6. Flip and cook for 2 to 3 minutes.

Serving Suggestions: Serve with ketchup.

Preparation & Cooking Tips: Cook in batches to avoid overcrowding.

Avocado Fries

Preparation Time: 10 minutes
Cooking Time: 10 minutes
Servings: 8

Ingredients:

- 2 avocados, sliced into strips

Dry mixture

- ½ cup breadcrumbs
- ½ teaspoon onion powder
- 1 teaspoon garlic powder
- ½ teaspoon paprika powder
- ½ teaspoon turmeric powder

Wet mixture

- ½ cup flour
- ½ teaspoon paprika powder
- ½ teaspoon turmeric powder
- ½ cup almond milk
- 1 teaspoon hot sauce

Method:

1. Mix dry mixture ingredients in a bowl.
2. In another bowl, combine wet mixture ingredients.
3. Dip each avocado strip into wet mixture, then cover with dry mixture.
4. Add to the air fryer basket.
5. Cook in the air fryer for 5 minutes.
6. Flip and cook for another 5 minutes.

Serving Suggestions: Serve with ketchup.

Preparation & Cooking Tips: Cook longer to make avocado fries extra crispy.

French Fries

Preparation Time: 15 minutes
Cooking Time: 25 minutes
Servings: 4

Ingredients:

- 1 lb. potatoes, sliced into strips
- Cooking spray
- Onion powder to taste
- Pinch cayenne pepper

Method:

1. Spray potato strips with oil.
2. Sprinkle with onion powder and cayenne pepper.
3. Add to the air fryer basket.
4. Cook at 375 degrees F for 15 minutes.
5. Flip and cook for another 10 minutes.

Serving Suggestions: Serve with ketchup.

Preparation & Cooking Tips: Soak potato strips in hot water for 10 minutes and then dry with paper towel before spraying with oil.

Banana Bread

Preparation Time: 40 minutes
Cooking Time: 40 minutes
Servings: 2

Ingredients:

- Cooking spray
- 1 cup all-purpose flour
- 1 teaspoon baking powder
- ¼ teaspoon baking soda
- 2 ripe bananas, pureed
- ¼ cup vegetable or canola oil
- ¼ cup granulated sugar
- 2 tablespoons peanut butter
- 2 tablespoons sour cream
- 1 teaspoon vanilla extract
- 1 egg, beaten

Method:

1. Preheat your air fryer to 330 degrees F.
2. Spray small loaf pan with oil.
3. Combine the remaining ingredients in a bowl.
4. Press mixture into the loaf pan.
5. Add loaf pan to the air fryer basket.
6. Cook for 40 minutes.

Serving Suggestions: Let cool before slicing and serving.

Preparation & Cooking Tips: Store in an airtight food container at room temperature for 1 week. Freeze bread for up to 4 months.

Pasta Chips

Preparation Time: 10 minutes

Cooking Time: 40 minutes

Servings: 8

Ingredients:

- 2 cups farfalle pasta, cooked according to package directions and drained
- 1 tablespoon olive oil
- 1 teaspoon Italian seasoning
- 2 teaspoons garlic powder

Method:

1. Preheat your air fryer to 400 degrees F.
2. Drizzle pasta with oil.
3. Sprinkle with Italian seasoning and garlic powder.
4. Arrange pasta in the air fryer basket.
5. Cook for 5 minutes.
6. Flip and cook for another 2 minutes.

Serving Suggestions: Let cool for 5 minutes before serving.

Preparation & Cooking Tips: Let pasta sit for 2 minutes after cooking in water and before drizzling with oil.

Crispy Chickpeas

Preparation Time: 10 minutes
Cooking Time: 15 minutes
Servings: 4

Ingredients:

- 19 oz. canned chickpeas, rinsed and drained
- 1 tablespoon olive oil
- ½ teaspoon paprika
- ¼ teaspoon onion powder
- ½ teaspoon garlic powder

Method:

1. Preheat your air fryer to 390 degrees F.
2. Toss chickpeas in olive oil.
3. Sprinkle with paprika, onion powder and garlic powder.
4. Place in the air fryer basket.
5. Air fry for 15 minutes, shaking every 5 minutes.

Serving Suggestions: Sprinkle with a little pepper before serving.

Preparation & Cooking Tips: You can also add cayenne pepper to the spice mixture.

Curly Zucchini Fries

Preparation Time: 15 minutes
Cooking Time: 20 minutes
Servings: 4

Ingredients:

- 1 zucchini
- Cooking spray
- 1 teaspoon Italian seasoning
- 1 cup breadcrumbs

Method:

1. Preheat your air fryer to 400 degrees F.
2. Use a spiralizer to slice the zucchini into spirals.
3. Spray the spirals with oil.
4. Season with Italian seasoning.
5. Dredge with breadcrumbs.
6. Place in the air fryer basket.
7. Cook for 10 minutes.

Serving Suggestions: Drain curly fries in a plate lined with paper towel before serving.

Preparation & Cooking Tips: You can also use other dried herbs to season zucchini fries.

Pakoras

Preparation Time: 10 minutes
Cooking Time: 20 minutes
Servings: 8

Ingredients:

- 2 cups cauliflower florets
- 1 ¼ cups chickpea flour
- 1 cup potatoes, minced
- ½ onion, chopped
- 1 clove garlic, minced
- ¾ cup water
- 1 teaspoon coriander
- 1 teaspoon curry powder
- ½ teaspoon cumin
- Pepper to taste
- Cooking spray

Method:

1. Add cauliflower florets to a food processor.
2. Pulse until fully ground.
3. Transfer to a bowl.
4. Add the rest of the ingredients.
5. Preheat your air fryer to 350 degrees F.
6. Form patties from the mixture.
7. Spray with oil.
8. Add to the air fryer basket.
9. Air fry for 8 minutes.
10. Flip and cook for another 7 minutes.

Serving Suggestions: Drain on a paper towel lined plate before serving.

Preparation & Cooking Tips: Cook in batches to avoid overcrowding.

Onion Rings

Preparation Time: 10 minutes
Cooking Time: 16 minutes
Servings: 4

Ingredients:

- 1 onion, sliced into thick rings
- Cooking spray
- ½ teaspoon garlic powder
- ½ teaspoon paprika
- 3 tablespoons almond flour
- 3 tablespoons coconut flour

Method:

1. Preheat your air fryer to 400 degrees F.
2. Spray onion rings with oil.
3. Season with garlic powder and paprika.
4. In a bowl, mix the two flours.
5. Cover the onion rings with flour mixture.
6. Add to the air fryer basket and cook for 16 minutes.

Serving Suggestions: Serve with sweet chili sauce.

Preparation & Cooking Tips: Do not overcrowd the air fryer basket. Cook in batches if necessary.

Potato Wedges

Preparation Time: 10 minutes

Cooking Time: 15 minutes

Servings: 4

Ingredients:

- 2 large potatoes, sliced into wedges
- 1 ½ tablespoons olive oil
- ½ teaspoon chili powder
- ½ teaspoon parsley flakes
- ½ teaspoon paprika
- Pepper to taste

Method:

1. Preheat your air fryer to 400 degrees F.
2. Toss potato wedges in oil.
3. Season with chili powder, parsley, paprika and pepper.
4. Add to the air fryer basket.
5. Air fry for 10 minutes.
6. Flip and cook for another 5 minutes.

Serving Suggestions: Serve with light garlic mayo dip.

Preparation & Cooking Tips: Arrange potato wedges in a single layer to cook evenly.

Sweet Potato Fries

Preparation Time: 20 minutes
Cooking Time: 25 minutes
Servings: 4

Ingredients:

- 2 sweet potatoes, sliced into strips
- 2 tablespoons olive oil

Seasoning mixture

- 1 tablespoon ground fennel
- 2 tablespoons ground coriander
- 1 tablespoon dried oregano
- Pepper to taste

Method:

1. Combine seasoning mixture ingredients in a bowl. Set aside.
2. Preheat your air fryer to 350 degrees F.
3. Toss sweet potato strips in oil.
4. Sprinkle with seasoning mixture.
5. Add to the air fryer basket.
6. Cook for 15 minutes.
7. Flip and cook for another 10 minutes.

Serving Suggestions: Serve with spicy dipping sauce.

Preparation & Cooking Tips: You can add cayenne pepper to the spice mixture.

Roasted Peanuts

Preparation Time: 5 minutes

Cooking Time: 20 minutes

Servings: 8

Ingredients:

- 2 tablespoons olive oil
- ½ teaspoon cayenne pepper
- 3 teaspoons Old Bay seasoning
- 8 oz. raw peanuts

Method:

1. Preheat your air fryer to 320 degrees F.
2. Combine oil, cayenne pepper and Old Bay seasoning in a bowl.
3. Toss peanuts in the mixture.
4. Add to the air fryer basket.
5. Air fry for 10 minutes.
6. Cook for 10 more minutes.

Serving Suggestions: Drain in a plate lined with paper towel before serving.

Preparation & Cooking Tips: Roasted peanuts can be stored in an airtight container for up to 4 days.

Chapter 9: Desserts

Fried Butter Cake

Preparation Time: 10 minutes
Cooking Time: 15 minutes
Servings: 4

Ingredients:

- Cooking spray
- 7 tablespoons vegan butter
- ¼ cup white sugar
- 1 egg, beaten
- 1 ⅔ cups all-purpose flour
- 6 tablespoons almond milk

Method:

1. Preheat your air fryer to 350 degrees F.
2. Spray your cake pan with oil.
3. Add butter to a bowl and beat using a mixer until creamy.
4. Stir in the egg and beat until fluffy.
5. Add flour and mix.
6. Pour in milk.
7. Mix well.
8. Pour into the cake pan.
9. Add the cake pan to the air fryer basket.
10. Air fry for 15 minutes.
11. Invert cake and serve.

Serving Suggestions: Let cool, slice and serve.

Preparation & Cooking Tips: Make sure cake pan fits in the air fryer basket.

Apple Crisp

Preparation Time: 10 minutes
Cooking Time: 15 minutes
Servings: 2

Ingredients:

- 2 apples, chopped
- 1 teaspoon cinnamon
- 2 tablespoons coconut sugar
- 1 teaspoon lemon juice

Topping

- 2 ½ tablespoons flour
- 3 tablespoons old fashioned oats
- 2 tablespoons butter

Method:

1. Preheat your air fryer to 350 degrees F.
2. Combine apples, cinnamon, sugar and lemon juice in a bowl.
3. Add mixture to a small baking pan.
4. Cover baking pan with foil.
5. Air fry for 10 minutes.
6. Mix topping ingredients in a bowl.
7. Pour mixture over the apples and spread.
8. Air fry for another 5 minutes.

Serving Suggestions: Drizzle with maple syrup before serving.

Preparation & Cooking Tips: Use cold firm butter for this recipe.

Cinnamon Donuts

Preparation Time: 20 minutes
Cooking Time: 15 minutes
Servings: 4

Ingredients:

- ¼ cup almond
- 1 ¼ cups all-purpose flour
- ¾ teaspoon baking powder
- 1/3 cup sugar
- 4 tablespoons vegan butter

Method:

1. Grind almond in food processor.
2. Add to a bowl.
3. Stir in the rest of the ingredients except cinnamon.
4. Use a mixer to blend well.
5. Knead the dough.
6. Form balls from the mixture.
7. Make a hole in the middle of the balls.
8. Add donuts to the air fryer basket.
9. Air fry at 350 degrees F for 8 minutes.
10. Flip and cook for 4 minutes.

Serving Suggestions: Sprinkle with cinnamon powder.

Strawberry Crisp

Preparation Time: 10 minutes
Cooking Time: 20 minutes
Servings: 1

Ingredients:

- 1 cup strawberry, chopped
- 1 tablespoon honey
- ¼ cup all-purpose flour
- 1 tablespoon coconut sugar

Method:

1. Mix strawberry, honey, flour and sugar in the air fryer.
2. Air fry at 350 degrees F for 15 minutes.
3. Stir and air fry for another 5 minutes.

Serving Suggestions: Drizzle with a little bit of honey before serving.

Preparation & Cooking Tips: You can also use other berries for this recipe.

Air Fried Choco Sandwich Cookies

Preparation Time: 5 minutes
Cooking Time: 8 minutes
Servings: 8

Ingredients:

- ⅓ cup water
- ½ cup pancake mix
- Cooking spray
- 8 chocolate sandwich cookies

Method:

1. Blend water and pancake mix.
2. Dip sandwich cookies in the mixture.
3. Add to the air fryer basket.
4. Cook in the air fryer at 400 degrees F for 5 minutes.
5. Flip and cook for 3 minutes.

Serving Suggestions: Sprinkle with a little confectioner's sugar before serving.

Preparation & Cooking Tips: Cook longer for crispier cookie.

Fruit Crumble

Preparation Time: 15 minutes
Cooking Time: 15 minutes
Servings: 2

Ingredients:

- 1 apple, diced
- ½ cup blueberries, sliced
- 2 tablespoons vegan butter
- 2 tablespoons coconut sugar
- ½ teaspoon ground cinnamon
- ¼ cup brown rice flour

Method:

1. Preheat your air fryer to 350 degrees F.
2. Add fruits in a small baking pan.
3. In a bowl, mix the remaining ingredients.
4. Pour mixture over the fruits.
5. Add baking pan to the air fryer basket.
6. Air fry for 15 minutes.

Serving Suggestions: Let cool before serving.

Preparation & Cooking Tips: You can also sprinkle a little more flour on top before cooking.

Roasted Bananas

Preparation Time: 5 minutes

Cooking Time: 8 minutes

Servings: 2

Ingredients:

- 2 bananas, sliced into rounds
- Cooking spray

Method:

1. Line your air fryer basket with parchment paper.
2. Preheat your air fryer to 375 degrees F.
3. Add the banana slices to the air fryer basket.
4. Spray with oil.
5. Air fry for 5 minutes.
6. Flip and cook for another 3 minutes.

Serving Suggestions: Drizzle with honey before serving.

Preparation & Cooking Tips: Use avocado cooking spray for this recipe.

Peach Crisp

Preparation Time: 15 minutes
Cooking Time: 20 minutes
Servings: 6

Ingredients:

Filling:

- 6 peaches, sliced in half
- 1 tablespoon coconut sugar
- 1 teaspoon ground cinnamon
- ½ tablespoon butter, sliced into cubes

Topping:

- ½ cup all purpose flour
- ½ cup coconut sugar
- ¼ teaspoon cinnamon powder
- ¼ cup vegan butter, sliced into cubes

Method:

1. Add peaches to a small cake pan.
2. Stir in the rest of the filling ingredients.
3. In a bowl, mix the topping ingredients.
4. Spread topping over the peach mixture.
5. Air fry at 350 degrees F for 20 minutes.

Serving Suggestions: Let cool before slicing and serving.

Preparation & Cooking Tips: Surface should be brown when done.

French Toast Sticks

Preparation Time: 10 minutes
Cooking Time: 10 minutes
Servings: 2

Ingredients:

- ½ teaspoon ground nutmeg
- 1 teaspoon vanilla extract
- 1 teaspoon cinnamon
- ¼ cup almond milk
- 4 slices bread, sliced into sticks

Method:

1. Line your air fryer basket with parchment paper.
2. Preheat your air fryer to 360 degrees F.
3. Combine all ingredients except bread sticks in a bowl.
4. Dip bread sticks into the mixture.
5. Air fry for 5 minutes.
6. Flip and cook for another 5 minutes.

Serving Suggestions: Sprinkle with a little more cinnamon powder before serving.

Preparation & Cooking Tips: Use stale bread for this recipe.

Caramelized Plum

Preparation Time: 5 minutes

Cooking Time: 15 minutes

Servings: 2

Ingredients:

- 1 lb. plum, sliced in half
- 1 tablespoon maple syrup
- ½ tablespoons coconut sugar
- ¼ teaspoon cinnamon powder

Method:

1. Line your air fryer with parchment paper.
2. Brush plum with maple syrup.
3. Sprinkle with sugar and cinnamon.
4. Air fry at 350 degrees F for 15 minutes.

Serving Suggestions: Drizzle with a little maple syrup before serving.

Preparation & Cooking Tips: You can also skip sugar if you like.

Conclusion

Holistic Anti-Inflammatory Meal Prep cookbook puts you on the path to good health by showing you how to reduce inflammation by following an anti-inflammatory diet. Keep it simple, satisfying and inflammation-fighting recipes.it is an indispensable anti-inflammatory diet cookbook and meal plan with one goal: to transition you to a healthier lifestyle that supports your immune system. Discover how an autoimmune diet can be easy, convenient and filled with variety and flavor.

The Anti-Inflammatory Meal Prep cookbook gets you on track to support your health goals, control your inflammation, and still eat foods you enjoy.Thank you for buying this book.Now let's start your gourmet journey!

CPSIA information can be obtained
at www.ICGtesting.com
Printed in the USA
LVHW062307130222
711067LV00009B/272

9 781639 350346